7/92

THE KING AND US

EDITORIAL CARTOONS BY

WITH WHITE HOUSE TRANSCRIPT EXCERPTS BY
RICHARD M. NIXON

Edited by Les Guthman

CLYMER PUBLICATIONS • LOS ANGELES, CALIFORNIA

First Printing October, 1974
Second Printing December, 1974
Third Printing January, 1975

CLYMER PUBLICATIONS
LOS ANGELES, CALIFORNIA

WATCHMAN, WHAT OF THE NIGHT?
—*Isaiah*

For Frank Wills
who spotted the
Watergate burglars
and called the cops

I never dreamed that Richard Nixon and I would be collaborating on a book! Collaboration with Mr. Nixon on anything these days is risky at best.

However, in spite of the risks and in the interest of history and clarification of the transcripts, the decision was made to go ahead and co-author this work.

We are not life-long friends, nor do we agree philosophically on most political, social or economic questions. As a matter of fact, we have never met. Personally.

But, how can anyone who has read the transcripts of the White House tapes not admit to knowing more than he wishes to know about the former President?

His earthy syntax.

His ties to homes and family.

His unflagging loyalty to business friends and associates.

His unselfish nature in charitable causes totaling in one year $295.

His unswerving loyalty to America and the Capitalist system, particularly at election time.

His unselfish determination to preserve the President and only incidentally the Presidency.

His detailed lists to make sure his enemies were taken care of.

His opening the doors to Peking and Moscow and at the same time closing the door to the Oval Office.

His selfless devotion to executive privilege and to the Constitutional guarantee of separation of powers.

His sense of history, his tapes and documents.

And it is in his historical perspective that this book came into being. It was not written. It was drawn and taped.

Cartoonists today are working in the tradition of editorial cartoonists of the last 150 years. Goya portrayed the cruelties of the Napoleonic Wars against Spain. Louis-Philippe found himself impaled on the pen of Daumier instead of a revolutionary's spike. Nast's cartoons are credited with the routing of Boss Tweed and *his* gang of Plumbers from Tammany Hall. Herblock was drawing about civil rights when most people thought civil was Orville's brother at Kitty Hawk.

Editorial cartoonists are idealists, of another world. Political, social, and moral injustices are perceived as monstrosities. Put intensity of conviction in the hands of a determined artist and you have the basic ingredients of a cartoonist; to care and to care deeply; to sweep aside all the complexities and go to the basic issue; to take suspicions, coincidences and past events, and record them larger than life.

The editorial cartoons in this book began the day after the break-in of Democratic headquarters in the Watergate complex, five months prior to the Presidential election of 1972.

Charges of burglary, payoffs, conspiracy, obstruction of justice, perjury, all under the generic name of "Watergate," became commonplace.

The issue was not so much "Watergate" as it was the President. Mr. Nixon had been following a scenario; I had been just reading the newspapers. And finally, the transcripts were submitted as evidence of the President's innocence.

Fiction became fact; suspicion became indictment. This was no banana republic rip-off. This was the real thing.

The President directing coverup after coverup? He didn't write history, he taped it.

And as I read those transcripts, the editorial cartoons of the past two years came to life. All the larger-than-life characterizations were life size. The suppositions of two years ago unfortunately were true.

Charade became real life; or was it the other way around?

John Tenniel, who illustrated "Alice in Wonderland," would have had problems here. After all — how do you caricature Alice's Wonderland? — with reality?

Why not? The grotesque had become charming; the charming grotesque.

The unthinkable thinkable.

And that final irony, that the King should indict himself with his own words.

September 1, 1974

THE KING AND US

WATERGATE

P Is there a higher up?

D Is there a higher up?

P Let's face it, I think they are really after Haldeman.

D Haldeman and Mitchell.

P Colson is not big enough name for them. He really isn't. He is, you know, he is on the government side, but Colson's name doesn't bother them so much. They are after Haldeman and after Mitchell. Don't you think so?

Meeting: The President, Haldeman and Dean.
Oval Office. March 13, 1973.

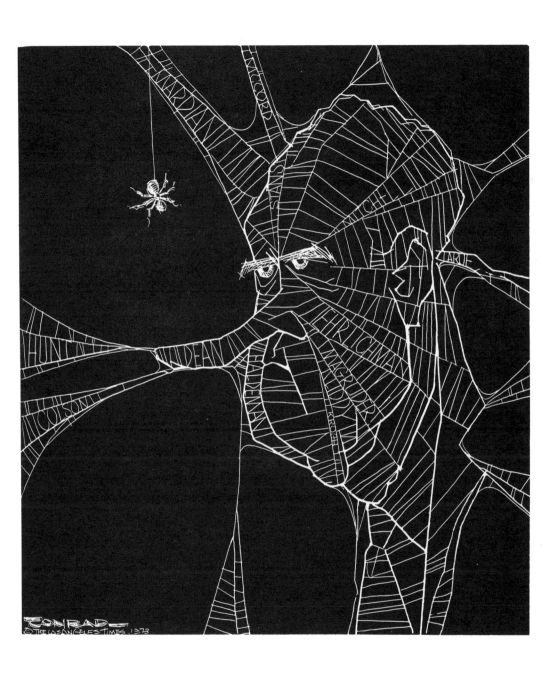

H What has happened on the bug?

P What bug?

D The second bug there was a bug found in the telephone of one of the men at the DNC.

P You don't think it was left over from the other time?

Meeting: The President, Haldeman, and Dean. Oval Office. September 15, 1972.

4

"He says he's from the phone company . . ."

P I don't know. But that's, uh, you know, up to this point, the whole theory has been containment, as you know, John.

M Yeah.

P And now, now we're shifting. As far as I'm concerned, actually from a personal standpoint, if you weren't making a personal sacrifice—it's unfair — Haldeman and Dean. That's what Eisenhower — that's all he cared about. He only cared about — Christ, "be sure he was clean." Both in the fund thing and the Adams thing. But I don't look at it that way. And I just — That's the thing I am really concerned with. We're going to protect our people, if we can.

M Well, the important thing is to get you up above it for this first operation. And then to see where the chips fall and, uh, and, uh, get through this grand jury thing up here.

Meeting: The President, Haldeman, Ehrlichman, Mitchell, and Dean. E.O.B. Office. March 22, 1973.

"Oh, nothing much . . . what's new with you, John?"

P Well, so be it. I noticed in the news summary Buchanan was viewing with alarm the grave crisis in the confidency of the Presidency, etc.

D Well the best way —

P How much?

D Pardon?

P How much of a crisis? It will be—I am thinking in terms of—the point is, everything is a crisis. (expletive deleted) it is a terrible lousy thing—it will remain a crisis among the upper intellectual types, the soft heads, our own, too—Republicans — and the Democrats and the rest. Average people won't think it is much of a crisis unless it affects them. (unintelligible)

D I think it will pass.

Meeting: The President, Haldeman, and Dean.
Oval Office. March 13, 1973.

"The average American is just like the child in the family . . . !"

E Mitchell kept lobbing out little tidbits about Colson's operation.

P Hmmm.

E About sending rioters up to the Capitol steps and other things that he knew about.

P Well, that was separate from all of Mitchell's stuff, though, wasn't it? What Colson did?

E Well, he was saying it's really too bad that all this is coming out because there's so much sordid stuff that will be (unintelligible) to the White House.

Meeting: The President, Haldeman, and Ehrlichman. Oval Office. April 14, 1973.

"I PRAY HEAVEN TO BESTOW THE BEST OF BLESSINGS ON THIS HOUSE AND ALL THAT HEREAFTER INHABIT IT. MAY NONE BUT HONEST AND WISE MEN EVER RULE UNDER THIS ROOF."

PRAYER BY PRES. JOHN ADAMS

D Now we've got Kalmbach. Kalmbach received, at the close of the '68 campaign in January of 1969, he got a million $700,000 to be custodian for. That came down from New York, and was placed in safe deposit boxes here. Some other people were on the boxes. And ultimately, the money was taken out to California. Alright, there is knowledge of the fact that he did start with a million seven. Several people know this. Now since 1969, he has spent a good deal of this money and accounting for it is going to be very difficult for Herb. For example, he has spent close to $500,000 on private polling. That opens up a whole new thing. It is not illegal, but more of the same thing.

P Everybody does polling.

D That's right. There is nothing criminal about it. It's private polling.

Meeting: The President, Haldeman, and Dean.
Oval Office. March 21, 1973.

"...$100,000 ...$200,000 ...$300,000 ...$400,000 ..."

P My view though is to say nothing about them on the ground that the matter is still in the courts and on appeal. Second, my view is to say nothing about the hearings at this point, except that I trust they will be conducted the proper way and I will not comment on the hearings while they are in process. Of course if they break through – if they get muckraking – It is best not to cultivate that thing here in the White House. If it is done at the White House again they are going to drop the (adjective deleted) thing. Now there, of course, you say but you leave it all to them. We'll see as time goes on. Maybe we will have to change our policy. But the President should not become involved in any part of this case. Do you agree with that?

D I agree totally, sir. Absolutely. That doesn't mean that quietly we are not going to be working around the office. You can rest assured that we are not going to be sitting quietly.

P I don't know what we can do. The people who are most disturbed about this (unintelligible) are the (adjective deleted) Republicans. A lot of these Congressmen, financial contributors, et cetera, are highly moral. The Democrats are just sort of saying, "(Expletive deleted) fun and games!"

Meeting: The President and Dean.
Oval Office. February 28, 1973.

"God save thee, Ancient Mariner . . ."

P Shows you what a master Dick Tuck is. Segretti's hasn't been a bit similar.

D They are quite humorous as a matter of fact.

P As a matter of fact, it is just a bunch of (characterization deleted). We don't object to such damn things anyway. On, and on and on. No, I tell you this it is the last gasp of our hardest opponents. They've just got to have something to squeal about it.

D It is the only thing they have to squeal —

P (Unintelligible) They are going to lie around and squeal. They are having a hard time now. They got the hell kicked out of them in the election. There is not a Watergate around in this town, not so much our opponents, even the media, but the basic thing is the establishment. The establishment is dying, and so they've got to show that despite the successes we have had in foreign policy and in the election, they've got to show that it is just wrong just because of this. They are trying to use this as the whole thing.

Meeting: The President, Haldeman, and Dean.
Oval Office. March 13, 1973.

A lonely President playing the piano late in the night.

"Pat, it's raining on my parade!"

P We are all in it together. This is a war. We take a few shots and it will be over. We will give them a few shots and it will be over. Don't worry. I wouldn't want to be on the other side right now. Would you?

D Along that line, one of the things I've tried to do, I have begun to keep notes on a lot of people who are emerging as less than our friends because this will be over some day and we shouldn't forget the way some of them have treated us.

P I want the most comprehensive notes on all those who tried to do us in. They didn't have to do it. If we had had a very close election and they were playing the other side I would understand this. No—they were doing this quite deliberately and they are asking for it and they are going to get it. We have not used the power in this first four years as you know. We have never used it. We have not used the Bureau and we have not used the Justice Department but things are going to change now. And they are either going to do it right or go.

D What an exciting prospect.

P Thanks. It has to be done.

Meeting: The President, Haldeman, and Dean. Oval Office. September 15, 1972.

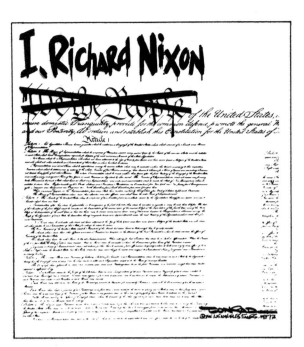

Anonymous letter received by the Washington Post, Sept. 15, 1972.

P I wouldn't want to be in Edward Bennett Williams', Williams' position after this election.

D No. No.

P None of these bastards —

D He, uh, he's done some rather unethical things that have come to light already, which in — again, Richey has brought to our attention.

P Yeah.

D He went down —

H Keep a log on all that.

D Oh, we are, on these. Yeah.

P Yeah.

H Because afterwards that is the guy.

P We're going after him.

H That is the guy we've got to ruin.

Meeting: The President, Haldeman, and Dean.
Oval Office. September 15, 1972.

His own worst enemy.

P Well, one hell of a lot of people don't give one damn about this issue of the suppression of the press, etc. We know that we aren't trying to do it. They all squeal about it. It is amusing to me when they say—I watched the networks and I thought they were restrained. What (expletive omitted) do they want them to do—go through the 1968 syndrome when they were 8 to 1 against us. They are only three to one this time. It is really sickening though to see these guys. These guys have always figured: "Well, we have the press on our side." You know we receive a modest amount of support—no more. Colson sure making them move it around, saying we don't like this or that and (inaudible)

Meeting: The President and Dean.
Oval Office. February 28, 1973.

★ WANTED ★

NAME: WALTER CRONKITE, CBS NEWS.

ALIAS: JOHN CHANCELLOR, DAVID BRINKLEY, TOM BROKAW, NBC;
ERIC SEVAREID, DAN RATHER, DANIEL SCHORR, CBS;
HARRY REASONER, ABC.

CHARGED WITH REPORTING: WATERGATE BREAK-IN AND COVER-UP;
OBSTRUCTION OF JUSTICE; COMPILING ENEMY LIST; FAKING OF
STATE DEPT CABLES; PERJURY (NUMBER OF COUNTS UNDER
INVESTIGATION); WIRETAPPING; SECRET CAMPAIGN FUNDS;
THE ITT SETTLEMENT; GOVERNMENT FUNDING TO IMPROVE
HOMES AT SAN CLEMENTE AND KEY BISCAYNE; NUMEROUS
RESIGNATIONS OF WHITE HOUSE STAFF; FINANCIAL DEALS
AND RESIGNATION OF SPIRO AGNEW; JUSTICE DEPT RESIGNATIONS.

ARMED AND DANGEROUS WITH MICROPHONES AND CAMERAS.

· NOTIFY ·
PROSECUTOR RICHARD M. NIXON
OR
LOCAL COMMITTEE TO REELECT THE PRESIDENT

© THE LOS ANGELES TIMES, 1973

P Hi, how are you? You had quite a day today, didn't you? You got Watergate on the way, didn't you?

D We tried.

H How did it all end up?

D Ah, I think we can say well at this point. The press is playing it just as we expect.

H Whitewash?

D No, not yet—the story right now—

P It is a big story.

H Five indicted plus the WH former guy and all that.

D Plus two White House fellows.

H That is good that takes the edge off whitewash really that was the thing Mitchell kept saying that to people in the country Liddy and Hunt were big men. Maybe that is good.

P How did MacGregor handle himself?

D I think very well he had a good statement which said that the Grand Jury had met and that it was now time to realize that some apologies may be due.

H Fat chance.

D Get the damn (inaudible)

H We can't do that.

P Just remember, all the trouble we're taking, we'll have a chance to get back one day.

Meeting: The President, Haldeman, and Dean. Oval Office. September 15, 1972.

"He's making his list, checking it twice, gonna' find out who's naughty and nice . . ."

P Let's not drag up, (unintelligible) the wagons up around the White House. Let me say it's got to be you, Ehrlichman, and I have got to put the wagons up around the President on this particular conversation. I just wonder if the son-of-a-bitch had a recorder on him. (tape noise) I didn't notice any, but I wasn't looking (unintelligible).

H It's almost inconceivable that the guy would try that, because . . .

P He was really coming in, in fact, to warn me.

H Yeah. He wasn't coming in, wasn't coming in for the purpose of . . .

P At that point, he hadn't made the command decision to, uh . . .

H He had no thought that you were going to say anything like this. All he was coming in to tell you was that there was a problem. He wasn't expecting you to solve it, uh, uh, to solve it that way. I think you probably surprised him enormously by, by even raising this point. And I think that is a . . .

P What? What?

H Oh, you know, well, we could get the money.

P Yeah.

H I think that's the last thing he expected you to say.

Meeting: The President and Haldeman.
E.O.B. Office. April 25, 1973.

Psychological profile of Watergate

H Right. You look at Gordon Strachan. Here's a little, young lawyer, who used to work for John Mitchell in his law firm, and came down to Washington to work in the government, and he's working under a campaign with the Attorney General of the United States in charge of it. Now how the hell do you expect him to decide whether something that's being done is right or wrong?

Meeting: The President and Haldeman.
March 22, 1973.

You know nothing about Watergate. Which group would you most likely suspect of burglary, theft, breaking and entering, wiretapping, election law violations and conspiracy?

P There is no question what they are after. What the Committee is after is somebody at the White House. They would like to get Haldeman or Colson, Ehrlichman.

D Or possibly Dean.—You know, I am a small fish.

Meeting: The President and Dean.
Oval Office. February 27, 1973.

Watergate

P We better get the other things out of the way. I think we're going to be—I don't want to be hammered—(unintelligible) I don't want to—I don't (unintelligible) they'll hammer the hell out of us anyway, but I don't (unintelligible) that's a — that's just a (unintelligible) all here. We'll take — we'll take a hell of a beating (unintelligible) in the next thirty days, a lot of heat, we'll take with regard to why we aren't appearing, why we aren't going to appear before the Committee. Now, how do we answer that? Do we answer that by saying the Committee won't agree to our — to the proper ground rules? Is that correct?

E We say we don't want to turn it into a circus. We want our testimony received in a judicious and probitive way. We are willing to have our people go, but only under the right circumstances.

P Well.

H You get it by the Kissinger thing we are releasing the record of your negotiations down channel.

P Yeah.

H Simply say that this is what we offer.

P Yeah.

H We stand ready to meet this offer whenever the enemy is willing to talk.

E Seriously.

P The question would then arise.

H Tell 'em we'll resume the bombing.

Meeting: The President, Haldeman, and Ehrlichman. Oval Office. April 14, 1973.

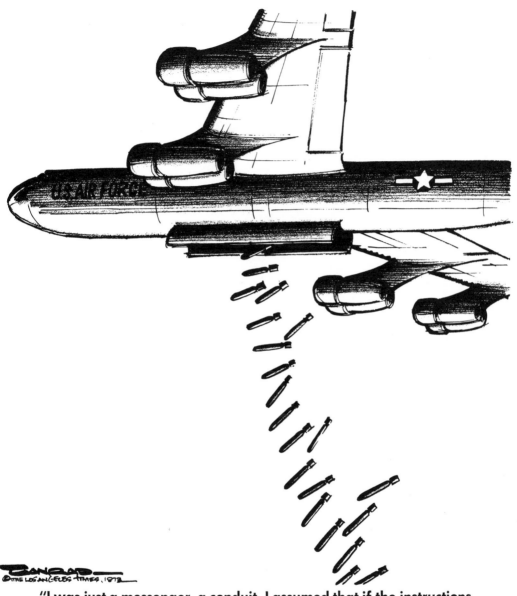

"I was just a messenger, a conduit. I assumed that if the instructions came from the White House, what I was doing must be authorized and legal and proper."   —Watergate testimony

P Why isn't it under civil rights statutes for these clowns demonstrating against us?

D I have argued for that very purpose.

P Really?

D Yes, I have.

P We were closer — nuts interfering with the campaign.

D That is exactly right.

Meeting: The President, Haldeman and Dean. Oval Office. March 21, 1973.

THE COVER-UP

D Three months ago I would have had trouble predicting there would be a day when this would be forgotten, but I think I can say that 54 days from now nothing is going to come crashing down to our surprise.

P That what?

D Nothing is going to come crashing down to our surprise.

P Oh well, this is a can of worms as you know a lot of this stuff that went on. And the people who worked this way are awfully embarrassed. But the way you have handled all this seems to me has been very skillful putting your fingers in the leaks that have sprung here and sprung there. The Grand Jury is dismissed now?

Meeting: The President, Haldeman, and Dean.
Oval Office. September 15, 1973.

"... Four more weeks! ... Four more weeks! ..."

D I think we can too. Here is what is happening right now. What sort of brings matters to the (unintelligible). One, this is going to be a continual blackmail operation by Hunt and Liddy and the Cubans. No doubt about it. And McCord, who is another one involved. McCord has asked for nothing. McCord did ask to meet with somebody, with Jack Caulfield who is his old friend who had gotten him hired over there. And when Caulfield had him hired, he was a perfectly legitimate security man. And he wanted to talk about commutation, and things like that. And as you know Colson has talked indirectly to Hunt about commutation. All of these things are bad, in that they are problems, they are promises, they are commitments. They are the very sort of thing that the Senate is going to be looking most for. I don't think they can find them, frankly.

P Pretty hard.

D Pretty hard. Damn hard. It's all cash.

P Pretty hard I mean as far as the witnesses are concerned.

Meeting: The President, Haldeman, and Dean. Oval Office. March 21, 1973.

Speaking of crime in the streets . . .

D Right.

So that is it. That is the extent of the knowledge. So where are the soft spots on this? Well, first of all, there is the problem of the continued blackmail which will not only go on now, but it will go on while these people are in prison, and it will compound the obstruction of justice situation. It will cost money. It is dangerous. People around here are not pros at this sort of thing. This is the sort of thing Mafia people can do: washing money, getting clean money, and things like that. We just don't know about those things, because we are not criminals and not used to dealing in that business.

P That's right.

D It is a tough thing to know how to do.

P Maybe it takes a gang to do that.

D That's right. There is a real problem as to whether we could even do it. Plus there is a real problem in raising money. Mitchell has been working on raising some money. He is one of the ones with the most to lose. But there is no denying the fact that the White House, in Ehrlichman, Haldeman and Dean are involved in some of the early money decisions.

P How much money do you need?

D I would say these people are going to cost a million dollars over the next two years.

P We could get that. On the money, if you need the money you could get that. You could get a million dollars. You could get it in cash. I know where it could be gotten. It is not easy, but it could be done. But the question is who the hell would handle it? Any ideas on that?

D That's right. Well, I think that is something that Mitchell ought to be charged with.

P I would think so too.

*Meeting: The President, Haldeman, and
Dean. Oval Office. March 21, 1973.*

". . . to uphold the Constitution and the laws of
the United States—as I see them . . ."

D Well, I have been a conduit for information on taking care of people out there who are guilty of crimes.

P Oh, you mean like the blackmailers?

D The blackmailers. Right.

P Well, I wonder if that part of it can't be—I wonder if that doesn't—let me put it frankly: I wonder if that doesn't have to be continued? Let me put it this way: let us suppose that you get the million bucks, and you get the proper way to handle it. You could hold that side?

D Uh, huh.

P It would seem to me that would be worthwhile.

D Well, that's one problem.

P I know you have a problem here. You have the problem with Hunt and his clemency.

D That's right. And you are going to have a clemency problem with the others. They all are going to expect to be out and that may put you in a position that is just untenable at some point. You know, the Watergate Hearings just over. Hunt now demanding clemency or he is going to blow. And politically, it's impossible for you to do it. You know, after everybody—

P That's right!

D I am not sure that you will ever be able to deliver on the clemency. It may be just too hot.

P You can't do it politically until after the '74 elections, that's for sure. Your point is that even then you couldn't do it.

D That's right. It may further involve you in a way you should not be involved in this.

P No—it is wrong that's for sure.

Meeting: The President, Haldeman, and Dean. Oval Office. March 21, 1973.

44

"As President, Jerry, you could grant me
clemency . . . but, it would be wrong!"

H Now that sort of finished the subject there and he got into the growing cancer business, and you said, "What do you mean?" He said, "Well, McCord would—Krogh perjured himself before the Grand Jury. He's haunted by it and went into that. Mitchell and Magruder have potential perjuries and there's a possibility of any individual blowing things (unintelligible)" Then you said, "Your major one to control is Hunt, because he knows so much." He said, "Right. He keeps saying Colson—he thinks Colson abandoned him, because he tried to see him about money and Colson wouldn't talk to him about money," and so on. And you said, "Looking at the immediate problem, don't you have to handle Hunt's financial situation?" And Dean said, "I talked to Mitchell about that last night." And you said, "We've got to keep the cap on the bottle that much, at least." Dean said, "That's right." You said, "Either that or let it all blow right now."

Meeting: The President and Haldeman.
E.O.B. Office. April 25, 1973.

P Well, if you had it, how would you get it to somebody?

D Well, I got it to LaRue by just leaving it in mail boxes and things like that. And someone phones Hunt to come and pick it up. As I say, we are a bunch of amateurs in that business.

H That is the thing that we thought Mitchell ought to be able to know how to find somebody who would know how to do all that sort of thing, because none of us know how to.

D That's right. You have to wash the money. You can get a $100,000 out of a bank, and it all comes in serialized bills.

P I understand.

D And that means you have to go to Vegas with it or a bookmaker in New York City. I have learned all these things after the fact. I will be in great shape for the next time around.

H (Expletive deleted)

P Well, the main point now is the people who will need the money (unintelligible). Well, of course, you've got the surplus from the campaign. That we have to account for. But if there's any other money hanging around —

Meeting: The President, Haldeman, and Dean. Oval Office. March 21, 1973.

KEY BISCAYNE   SAN CLEMENTE

UFO's

P The only thing we could do with him would be to parole him like the (unintelligible) situation. But you couldn't buy clemency.

D Kleindienst has now got control of the Parole Board, and he said to tell me we could pull Paroles off now where we couldn't before. So—

H Kleindienst always tells you that, but I never believe it.

P Paroles — let the (unintelligible) worry about that. Parole, in appearance, etc., is something I think in Hunt's case, you could do Hunt, but you couldn't do the others. You understand.

Meeting: The President, Haldeman and Dean. Oval Office. March 21, 1973.

"Yes, Hoffa did time here at Lewisburg . . . Why do you ask?"

P What is the answer on this? How you keep it out, I don't know. You can't keep it out if Hunt talks. You see the point is irrelevant. It has gotten to this point —

D You might put it on a national security grounds basis.

H It absolutely was.

D And say that this was —

H (unintelligible) — CIA—

D Ah —

H Seriously,

P National Security. We had to get information for national security grounds.

D Then the question is, why didn't the CIA do it or why didn't the FBI do it?

P Because we had to do it on a confidential basis.

H Because we were checking them.

P Neither could be trusted.

Meeting: The President, Haldeman and Dean. Oval Office. March 21, 1973.

Cloak and dagger

D It seems to me that I don't think Sullivan would give up the White House. Sullivan — if I have one liability in Sullivan here, it is his knowledge of the earlier (unintelligible) that occurred here.

P That we did?

D That we did.

P Well, why don't you just tell him — he could say, "I did no political work at all. My work in the Nixon Administration was solely in the national security." And that is thoroughly true!

D That is true.

P Well, good luck.

D Thank you, sir.

Meeting: The President, Haldeman and Dean. Oval Office. March 13, 1973.

"We're in this together, and don't you forget it!"

P It will look like the President

D Is covering up —

P Has covered up a huge (unintelligible)

D That's correct.

H But you can't (inaudible)

P You have now moved away from the hunker down —

Meeting: The President, Haldeman and Dean. Oval Office. March 21, 1973.

"Don't step on my tapes!"

P What about Ford? Do you think so? Connally can't because of the way he is set up. If anybody can do it, Connally could, but if Ford can get the minority members. They have some weak men and women on that committee, unfortunately. Heckler is alright.

D Heckler was great.

P Widnall, et cetera. Jerry should talk to Widnall. After all, if we ever win the House, Jerry will be the speaker and he could tell him if he did not get off. . . he will not be Chairman ever.

D That would be very helpful to get all of these people at least pulling together. If Jerry could get a little action on this.

H Damn it Jerry should.

Meeting: The President, Haldeman, and Dean
Oval Office. September 15, 1972.

"Jerry Ford's a nice guy, but he's played too many games
without his helmet."—LBJ

Gerald R. Agnew

"Powerful pressure organizations . . .   are waging massive . . .

propaganda campaigns . . .   against the President!"

P When you talk to Kleindienst — because I have raised this (inaudible) thing with him on the Hiss Case — he has forgotten, I suppose. Go back and read the first chapter of SIX CRISES. But I know, as I said, that was espionage against the nation, not against the party. FBI, Hoover, himself, who's a friend of mine said "I am sorry I have been ordered not to cooperate with you" and they didn't give us one (adjective omitted) thing. I conducted that investigation with two (characterization omitted) committee investigators — that stupid — they were tenacious. We got it done.

Then we worked that thing. We then got the evidence, we got the typewriter, we got the Pumpkin Papers. We got all of that ourselves. The FBI did not cooperate. The Justice Department did not cooperate. The Administration would not answer questions except, of course, for Cabinet offers, I mean like Burling came down and some of the others.

D Funny, when the shoe is on the other foot how they look at things, isn't it?

Meeting: The President and Dean.
Oval Office. February 28, 1973.

Where are you, Whitaker Chambers,
now that we need you?

E The only thing that we can say is for Ziegler to say, "Look we've investigated backwards and forwards in the White House, and we're satisfied on the basis of the report we have that nobody in the White House has been involved in a burglary, nobody had notice of it, knowledge of it, participated in the planning or aided or abetted it in any way." Well that's what we could say and it happens to be true — as for that transaction.

P [Laughs] Sure. As for that transaction.

Meeting: The President, Haldeman, Ehrlichman and Dean. E.O.B. Office. March 21, 1973.

"Lights! Camera! Obfuscation!"

P Do you need any IRS stuff?

D There is no need at this hour for anything from IRS, and we have a couple of sources over there that I can go to. I don't have to go around with Johnnie Walters or anybody, but we can get right in and get what we need.

Meeting: The President, Haldeman, and Dean. Oval Office. March 13, 1973.

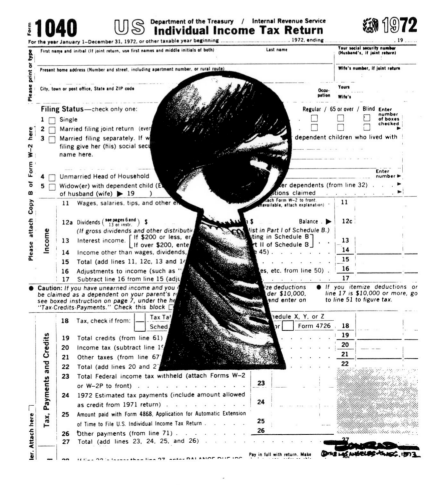

D Well if they say they have to hold up Gray's confirmation until the Watergate Hearings are completed —

P That's great!

D That's the vehicle.

P That's a vote really for us, because Gray, in my opinion, should not be the head of the FBI. After going through the hell of the hearings, he will not be a good Director, as far as we are concerned.

D I think that is true. I think he will be a very suspect Director. Not that I don't think Pat won't do what we want — I do look at him a little differently than Dick in that regard. Like he is still keeping in close touch with me. He is calling me. He has given me his hot line. We talk at night, how do you want me to handle this, et cetera? So he still stays in touch, and is still being involved, but he can't do it because he is going to be under such surveillance by his own people — every move he is making — that it would be a difficult thing for Pat. Not that Pat wouldn't want to play ball, but he may not be able to.

P I agree. That's what I meant.

Meeting: The President, Haldeman and Dean. Oval Office. March 13, 1973.

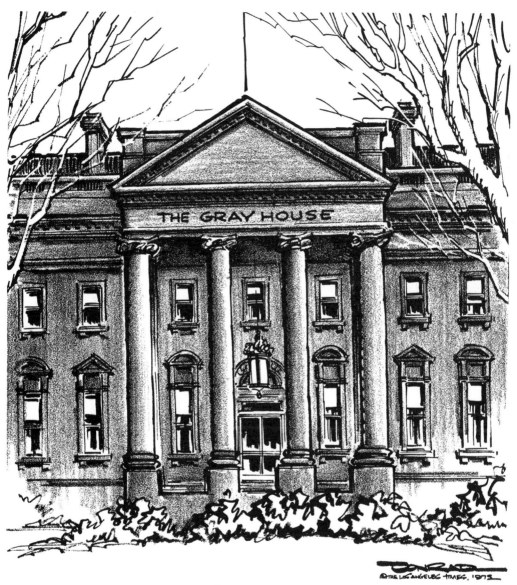

This is your FBI

D People get annoyed — some finger pointing — false accusations — any internal dissension of any nature.

P You mean on this case?

D On this case. There is some bitterness between the Finance Committee and the Political Committee — they feel they are taking all the heat and all the people upstairs are bad people — not being recognized.

Meeting: The President and Dean.
Oval Office. September 15, 1973.

"You're absolutely right, Bill . . . we'll get rid of the piano!"

D Sirica is a strange man. He is known as a hanging judge.

P (unintelligible)

D That's right. He's tough. He is tough.

Meeting: The President, Haldeman and Dean. Oval Office. March 13, 1973.

"Now, counselor, you were saying something about
'soft-headed, permissive' judges . . ."

THE COVER-UP
OF
THE COVER-UP

E I have reason to think Liddy has already talked.

H You know (unintelligible) so they're obviously moving on the cover-up.

P Yeah.

E If Mitchell went in, that might knock that whole week into a cocked hat.

P Why?

H Well, I'm not sure then they care about the cover-up any more.

P Well, they might.

E If Mitchell gave them a complete statement —

P I wish they wouldn't, but I think they would, Bob.

E If Mitchell gave them a complete statement.

P They shouldn't. You're right. The cover-up, he said that — well, basically it's a second crime. Isn't that right, John?

E Yes.

P Do you think they would keep going on the cover up even if Mitchell went in?

E Well, I would assume so. I would certainly assume so.

Meeting: The President, Haldeman, and Ehrlichman. E.O.B. Office. April 14, 1973.

O that I were as great as my grief, or lesser than my name!
Or that I could forget what I have been!
Or not remember what I must be now!

King Richard II, Act III, Scene III

P The question, of course, is Liddy and the others. But we shall see. It is the word of the felons against the word of the men that raised the money, huh?

H That's right. Well, you just — You don't know how much will come out in what way either. I mean that —

P No, we, at least I think now, we pretty much know what the worst is. I don't know what the hell else they could have that is any worse. You know what I mean. Unless there is something that I don't know, unless somebody's got a piece of paper that somebody signed or some damn thing, but that I doubt.

Telephone Conversation: The President, and Haldeman. April 14, 1973.

The Bill of Rights

To Nixon High Priority

As provided in the FIRST TEN AMENDMENTS TO THE CONSTITUTION OF THE UNITED STATES
Effective December 15, 1791

Preamble

The conventions of a number of the States having at the time of their adopting the Constitution, expressed a desire, in order to prevent misconstruction or abuse of its powers, that further declaratory and restrictive clauses should be added: And as extending the ground of public confidence in the Government, will best insure the beneficent ends of its institution.

1 **Right** *to Freedom of Religion, Speech, Press, Assembly, Petition.*
Congress shall make no law respecting an establishment of religion, or prohibiting the free exercise thereof; or abridging the freedom of speech, or of the press; or the right of the people peaceably to assemble, and to petition the Government for a redress of grievances. — *not in this time frame.*

2 **Right** *to Keep and Bear Arms.*
A well regulated Militia, being necessary to the security of a free State, the right of the people to keep and bear Arms, shall not be infringed. — *"national*

3 **Rights** *on Quartering of Soldiers.*
No Soldier shall, in time of peace, be quartered in any house, without the consent of the Owner, nor in time of war, but in a manner to be prescribed by law. — *Inoperative*

4 **Right** *against Unreasonable Search and Seizure.*
The right of the people to be secure in their persons, houses, papers, and effects, against unreasonable searches and seizures, shall not be violated, and no Warrants shall issue, but upon probable cause, supported by Oath or affirmation, and particularly describing the place to be searched, and the persons or things to be seized. — *negative*

5 **Right** *to Protection of Persons and Property.*
No person shall be held to answer for a capital, or otherwise infamous crime, unless on a presentment or indictment of a Grand Jury, except in cases arising in the land or naval forces, or in the Militia, when in actual service, in time of War or public danger; nor shall any person be subject for the same offense to be twice put in jeopardy of life or limb; nor shall be compelled in any Criminal Case to be a witness against himself, nor be deprived of life, liberty, or property, without due process of law; nor shall private property be taken for public use, without just compensation. — *doesn't wash*

6 **Rights** *of Persons Accused of Crime.*
In all criminal prosecutions, the accused shall enjoy the right to a speedy and public trial, by an impartial jury of the State and district wherein the crime shall have been committed, which districts shall have been previously ascertained by law, and to be informed of the nature and cause of the accusation; to be confronted with the witnesses against him; to have compulsory process for obtaining Witnesses in his favor, and to have the Assistance of Counsel for his defense. — *doesn't allop*

7 **Right** *of Trial by Jury.*
In suits at common law, where the value in controversy shall exceed twenty dollars, the right of trial by jury shall be preserved, and no fact tried by a jury shall be otherwise re-examined in any Court of the United States, than according to the rules of the common law. — *lowest priority*

8 **Right** *to Protection Against Excessive Fines, Bail, Punishment.*
Excessive bail shall not be required, nor excessive fines imposed, nor cruel and unusual punishment inflicted. — *inoperable*

9 **Rights** *not enumerated retained by the people.*
The enumeration in the Constitution of certain rights, shall not be construed to deny or disparage others retained by the people — *not in OUR game plan*

10 **Rights** *reserved to the States and the People.*
The powers not delegated to the United States by the Constitution, nor prohibited by it to the States, are reserved to the States respectively, or to the people. — *not viable*

CONRAD
© THE LOS ANGELES TIMES. 197

Memo from H. R. Haldeman to the President

P Then he can go over there as soon (unintelligible) this. But, uh, the, want to do is to—Now let me make this clear. I, I, I thought it was, uh, very, uh, very cruel thing as it turned out—although at the time I had to tell (unintelligible) —what happened to Adams. I don't want it to happen with Watergate—the Watergate matter. I think he made a, made a mistake, but he shouldn't have been sacked, he shouldn't have been—And, uh, for that reason, I am perfectly willing to—I don't give a shit what happens. I want you all to stonewall it, let them plead the Fifth Amendment, coverup or anything else, if it'll save it — save the plan. That's the whole point.

Meeting: The President, Ehrlichman, Mitchell, and Dean. E.O.B. Office. March 22, 1973.

The foundering fathers

H Okay, but you. You do have rules of evidence. You can refuse to, to talk—

D You can take the Fifth Amendment.

P That's right. That's right.

H You can say you forgot, too, can't you?

D Sure.

P That's right.

D But you can't—you're—very high risk in perjury situation.

P That's right. Just be damned sure you say I don't remember; I can't recall, I can't give any honest, an answer to that that I can recall.

Meeting: The President, Haldeman, and Dean.
Oval Office. March 21, 1973.

"... Richard M. who ...?"

P And Kleindienst owes Mitchell everything. Mitchell wanted him for Attorney General. Wanted him for Deputy, and here he is. Now, (expletive deleted). Baker's got to realize this, and that if he allows this thing to get out of hand he is going to potentially ruin John Mitchell. He won't. Mitchell won't allow himself to be ruined. He will put on his big stone face. But I hope he does and he will.

Meeting: The President and Dean.
Oval Office. February 28, 1973.

"Does that answer your question, Senator?"

P He will—how does he tell his story? He has a pretty hard row to hoe—he and Stans have.

D He will be good. Herb is the kind of guy who will check, not once nor twice, on his story—not three times—but probably fifty to a hundred times. He will go over it. He will know it. There won't be a hole in it. Probably he will do his own Q & A. He will have people cross-examine him from ten ways. He will be ready as John Mitchell will be ready, as Maury Stans will be ready.

P Mitchell is now studying, is he?

D He is studying. Sloan will be the worst witness. I think Magruder will be a good witness. This fellow, Bart Porter, will be a good witness. They have already been through Grand Jury. They have been through trial. They did well. And then, of course, people around here.

Meeting: The President, Haldeman, and Dean.
Oval Office. March 13, 1973.

"... 'Stonewalling' was one thing, Jeb, but this is ridiculous!"

E I'd say, you know, face up John. And, you know, I've listened to Magruder, and he's, in my opinion he's about to blow and that's the last straw.

P And, also, Hunt is going to testify, too, Monday, we understand.

E We've got to think of this thing from the standpoint of the President and I know you have been right along and that's the reason you've been conducting yourself as you have.

P Right.

E It's now time, I think, to rethink what best serves the President and also what best serves you in the ultimate outcome of this thing.

P Right.

E I think we have to recognize that you are not going to escape indictment. There's no way. Far better that you should be prosecuted on information from the U.S. Attorney based on your conversation with the U.S. Attorney, than on an indictment by a Grand Jury of 15 blacks and 3 whites after this kind of an investigation.

P Right. And the door of the White House. We're trying to protect it.

Meeting: The President, Haldeman, and Ehrlichman. E.O.B. Office. April 14, 1973.

"Grand Jur-ies are breaking up that old gang of mine . . ."

E Let's take it just as far as you call Mitchell to the Oval Office as, a —

P No.

E I'm essentially convinced that Mitchell will understand this thing.

P Right.

E And that if he goes in it redounds to the Administration's advantage. If he doesn't then we're —

P How does it redound to our advantage?

E That you have a report from me based on three weeks' work; that when you got it, you immediately acted to call Mitchell in as the provable wrong-doer, and you say, "My God, I've got a report here. And it's clear from this point that you are guilty as hell. Now, John, for (expletive deleted) sake go on in there and do what you should. And let's get this thing cleared up and get it off the country's back and move on." And—

H Plus the other side of this is that that's the only way to beat it now.

Meeting: The President, Haldeman, and Ehrlichman. E.O.B. Office. April 14, 1973.

"We could plea-bargain, but that would be wrong!"

H I would guess what's happened if he's got this report from, Colson does, from Danny Hofgren that at the bar in the Bahamas with (unintelligible), someone (unintelligible) one night said to Hofgren everybody was involved in this. He didn't—

E Everybody knew about it?

H Mitchell, Haldeman, Colson, Dean, the President

P Magruder—

E He said, he specifically said the President.

P Magruder does believe that, does he?

H No. I've got it—

P I just wonder if he believes (unintelligible). Does he believe it, John?

E No. He tape recorded this thing. Higby handled it so well that Magruder has closed all his doors now with this tape.

P What good will that do John?

E Sir, it beats the socks off him if he ever gets off the reservation.

P Can you use the tape?

E Well no. You can use Higby.

P Why not—

E Well, it's illegal.

Meeting: The President, Haldeman, and Ehrlichman. E.O.B. Office. April 14, 1973.

Crossing the Watergate

P Illegal? Of course not! Apparently you haven't been able to do anything on my project of getting on the offensive?

D But I have sir, to the contrary!

P Based on Sullivan, have you kicked a few butts around?

D I have all of the information that we have collected. There is some there, and I have turned it over to Baroody. Baroody is having a speech drafted for Barry Goldwater. And there is enough material there to make a rather sensational speech just by: Why in the hell isn't somebody looking into what happened to President Nixon during his campaign? Look at these events! How do you explain these? Where are the answers to these questions? But, there is nothing but threads. I pulled all the information.

P Also, the Senator should then present it to the Ervin Committee and demand that that be included. He is a Senator, a Senator . . .

D What I am working on there for Barry is a letter to Senator Ervin that this has come to my attention, and why shouldn't this be a part of the inquiry? And he can spring out 1964 and quickly to '72. We've got a pretty good speech there, if we can get out our materials.

P Good!

D So it's in the mill.

H We have finally started something.

Meeting: The President, Haldeman, and Dean.
Oval Office. March 13, 1973.

The creature from the Watergate Lagoon

K Thinking of Magruder as a primary witness type. You better be very careful what you do from here on out, John. Don't put yourself in the position of—

E Prejudicing anybody's rights.

K With respect to the Commission—

E That is why I am calling you, my dear.

K Your's is a very God damn delicate line as to what you do to get information to give to the President and what you can do in giving information to the Department of Justice, you know, to enforce the law.

E Well you are my favorite law enforcement officer.

K (unintelligible)

E Do you want me to give you anything additional on Monday?

K Who did you talk to, John?

E What do you mean? Mitchell and Magruder

K Those are the only two?

E Well, no I have been talking to people for three weeks. I have talked to everybody but the milkman.

Telephone Conversation: Ehrlichman and Kleindienst. April 14, 1973.

94

**Milk has something for every body
—even Richard Nixon's**

And all along we thought he was delivering milk!

P Nevertheless, that Hunt then saying there was a pay-off. All right. Hunt, on other activities—Hunt then according to Colson was not—I don't know what Colson meant about the door of the Oval office.

E I'll have to get back on that. Shapiro was there and I didn't want to get into it.

P Right.

H (Unintelligible).

P No, not. It was an earlier conversation about the Magruder conversation when Colson — I think the Magruder conversation from what I have seen related —

H Magruder doesn't go to the door of the Oval Office. He doesn't even come to visit me in the White House.

P I know. But he—it is Colson's view that Magruder's talking would have the effect of bringing it there because of the—I think what he is really referring to, John, is that by reason of Colson, by reason of Magruder nailing Haldeman and Colson, that that's the door of the Oval Office.

Meeting: The President, Haldeman, and Ehrlichman. E.O.B. Office. April 14, 1973.

The Oval Office

E We had this meeting, and, and, uh, he lobbed mud balls at the White House at every opportunity. It was very interesting how he dragged it in, uh, yeah, one after the other.

P . . . What in the name of Christ is this all about? Well, what it involves, of course, we have to be fair, it involves, uh, the highest, the king of the mountain.

E Yeah.

Meeting: The President and Ehrlichman.
Oval Office. April 14, 1973.

'King of the Mountain'

D Well you are probably going to get more questions this week. And the tough questions. And some of them don't have easy answers. For example, did Haldeman know that there was a Don Segretti out there? That question is likely.

P Did he? I don't know.

D Yes, he had knowledge that there was somebody in the field doing prankster-type activities.

P Well, I don't know anything about that. What about my taking, basically, just trying to fight this thing one at a time. I am only going to have to fight it later, and it is not going to get any better. I think the thing to say is, "this is a matter being considered by the Committee and I am not going to comment on it". I don't want to get into the business of taking each charge that comes up in the Committee and commenting on it: "It is being considered by the Committee. It is being investigated and I am not going to comment on it."

Meeting: The President, Haldeman, and Dean.
Oval Office. March 13, 1973.

The silent majority

E Uh, huh. Well, would you want to on television tomorrow?

P No, but the way I would do the television—I am not planning to do this before at 9 o'clock, on prime time. I would do this in the Oval Room; no make up at all. In other words, that's enough right there. What the hell, I could say I have done this, I have—I want to get to the bottom of this and what have you (unintelligible) OK, John? All right.

Meeting: The President, Haldeman, Ehrlichman and Ziegler. E.O.B. Office. March 27, 1973.

"I have nothing to hide!"

P As far as what happened up to this time, our cover there is just going to be the Cuban committee did this for them up through the election.

D Well, Yeah. We can put that together. That isn't, of course, quite the way it happened, but, uh—

P I know, but it's the way it's going to have to happen.

D It's going to have to happen. [Laughs.]

P That's right.

Meeting: The President, Haldeman, and Dean.
Oval Office. March 21, 1973.

P You've got to have something where it doesn't appear that I am doing this in, you know, just in a—saying to hell with the Congress and to hell with the people, we are not going to tell you anything because of Executive Privilege. That, they don't understand. But if you say, "No, we are willing to cooperate," and you've made a complete statement, but make it very incomplete. See, that is what I mean. I don't want a, too much in chapter and verse as you did in your letter, I just want just a general—

D An all around statement.

P That's right. Try just something general. Like "I have checked into this matter; I can categorically, based on my investigation, the following: Haldeman is not involved in this, that and the other thing. Mr. Colson did not do this; Mr. so and so did not do this. Mr. Blank did not do this." Right down the line, taking the most glaring things.

Telephone Conversation: The President, and Dean. March 20, 1973 .

"Well, if he won't pay any attention to Congress, what makes you think he'll pay any attention to us?"

"Stop me if you've heard this one . . . !"

E You could say this. You could say I have never had a communication with anybody on my staff about this burglary—

P Therefore—

E Or about Segretti, prior to—

P Segretti, Segretti is not in this court so that is no problem.

E Well—then all right—

P I have never had any—

E Since I had no communication with anybody on the White House staff about this burglary or about the circumstances leading up to it, there is no occasion for executive privilege in this matter.

P With regard to this, I want you to get to the bottom of it. So there will be no executive privilege on that. On other matters—

H And that takes you up to the June 17th. What do you do after June 17th?

P Use the executive privilege on that.

Meeting: The President, Haldeman, Ehrlichman, and Ziegler. E.O.B. Office. March 27, 1973.

"The tapes are covered by Executive privilege."

"The tapes are confidential."

"The tapes are ambiguous."

"The tapes do not exist."

P The Grand Jury thing has its in view of this thing. Suppose we have a Grand Jury thing. What would that do to the Ervin Committee? Would it go right ahead?

D Probably Probably.

P If we do that on a Grand Jury, we would then have a much better cause in terms of saying, "Look, this is a Grand Jury, in which the prosecutor—How about a special prosecutor? We could use Petersen, or use another one. You see he is probably suspect. Would you call in another prosecutor?

Meeting: The President, Haldeman, and Dean.
Oval Office. March 21, 1973.

The creation of an "independent prosecutor"

D They can subpoena any of us. There is no doubt about that. If they don't serve it here because they can't get in. They can serve you at home somewhere. They can always find you.

H We move to Camp David and hide! They can't get in there.

P Well, go ahead.

Meeting: The President, Haldeman, Ehrlichman, Dean, and Mitchell. E.O.B. Office. March 21, 1973.

P Oh yes, I remember. You told me that. I guess everybody told me that. Dean said, "I am not going down there and lie," because your hand will shake and your emotions. Remember you told me that.

D Yes, I said that. I am incapable of it.

P Thank God. Don't ever do it John. Tell the truth. That is the thing I have told everybody around here. (expletive omitted) tell the truth! All they do John is compound it.

P That (characterization omitted) Hiss would be free today if he hadn't lied. If he had said, "Yes I knew Chambers and as a young man I was involved with some Communist activities but I broke it off a number of years ago." And Chambers would have dropped it. If you are going to lie, you go to jail for the lie rather than the crime. So believe me, don't ever lie.

Meeting: The President and Dean.
Oval Office. April 16, 1973.

P Well, you fellows need a rest.

H Rest? There's that damn dinner.

E We'll grin at the White House correspondents.

H That's no rest, that's work.

P Well, a year from now. It will soon be different.

E Oh, yeah.

P Nope, seriously—

E Six months.

P Nope, sooner than you think. Let me tell you, John, the thing about all this that has concerned me is dragging the damn thing out. Dragging it out and being—and having it be the only issue in town. Now the thing to do now, have done. Indict Mitchell and all the rest and there'll be a horrible two weeks—a horrible, terrible scandal, worse than Teapot Dome and so forth.

Meeting: The President, Haldeman, and
Ehrlichman. E.O.B. Office. April 14, 1973.

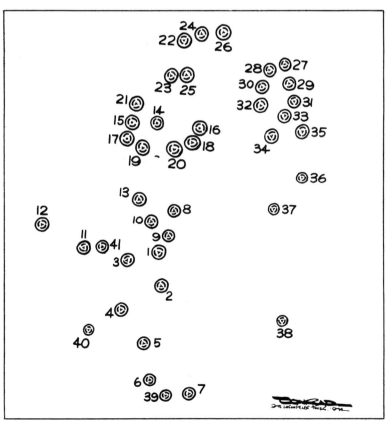

To find out who's dragging out Watergate, connect the 41 tapes.

D I agree. The scenario is for myself and for Dick (inaudible)—it is a record for the future.

P It is the record for the future. Maybe you can tell Ervin on the mountaintop that this is a good way to set up a procedure for the future. You know what I mean, where future cases of this sort are involved. We are making a lot of history here, Senator.

M And the Senator can be a great part of it.

P A lot of history.

Meeting: The President, Haldeman, Ehrlichman, Dean, and Mitchell. E.O.B. Office. March 22, 1973.

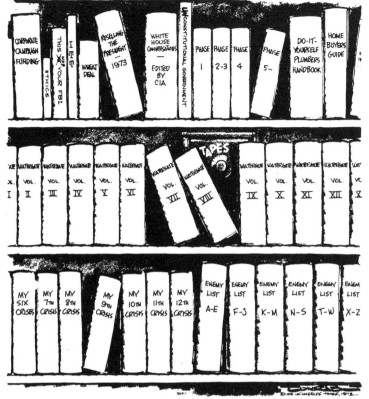

The Nixon library

Match each of the above with the
cause for which each is best known:

A. Gun controls   B. Election campaign reform
C. Indian rights   D. Prohibition

H Well, re Magruder over at Commerce. Obviously you would send a report over that said Magruder did this and that. Well, that is what he is talking about apparently.

P And then Magruder. The fellow is a free agent.

H The free agent.

P Who according to the Hunt theory, could pull others down with him.

H Sure. What would happen? Sure as hell we have to assume Dwight would be drawn in.

D Draw numbers with names out of a hat to see who gets hurt and who doesn't. That sounds about as fair as you can be, because anyone can get hurt.

Meeting: The President, Haldeman, Ehrlichman, and Dean. E.O.B. Office. March 21, 1973.

"The press won't have—let's see now—Bob Haldeman, John
Ehrlichman, Jeb Magruder, Richard Kleindienst, John Dean
or Patrick Gray to kick around anymore!"

P We can't get the President involved in this. His people, that is one thing. We don't want to cover up, but there are ways. And then he's got to say, for example? You start with him certainly on the business of obstruction of justice.

E That's right.

P Look, John—we need a plan here. And so that LaRue, Mardian and the others—I mean,

E Well, I am not sure I can go that far with him.

P No. He can make the plan up.

E I will sound it out.

P Right. Get a good night's sleep.

E Thank you, Sir.

P I'll bet you do. You know in a way it is a curious thing—not curious at all—but, John, while it is terribly painful, of course, to go to that dinner tonight—while it is painful, I just feel better about getting the damn thing done. Or do you agree?

E Absolutely.

P I mean, after all, it is my job and I don't want the Presidency tarnished, but also I am a law enforcement man.

Telephone Conversation: The President, and Ehrlichman. April 14, 1973.

"When we fail to make the criminal pay for his crime, we
encourage him to think that crime will pay."

P Now here you've got the—I was just looking in the paper this morning. Saxbe, Mathias, Johnny Rhodes, John Anderson, other persons. Two or three of those names are not new, but they're all there. They are trying to build that up as a chorus of Republicans and more to come.

E It'll be five a day until next month.

Meeting: The President, Haldeman, and Ehrlichman. E.O.B. Office. April 14, 1973.

"Patty Hearst is a crook . . . I know a crook when I see one!"

E I said, "Now you should know that Kleindienst has said that if you in any way get cracked in this case that he is going to step aside, regardless of the case. I understand Henry Petersen also will." And I said, "That the thing Kleindienst is pushing for is a special prosecutor." John said, "That would be a grave mistake because it would be subversive to the orderly process of justice if everytime you had an important case you strive to put the matter in an ad hoc process."

P Well, I particularly—the present prosecutor (unintelligible).

E So I said, "At least, he thought he should step aside." He got a very wide smile on his face, and he said, "Well, it's great to have friends isn't it?" He says, "Especially the way we stuck by them"— meaning the I.T.T. business, I assume, because of Kleindienst. So that was an interesting little aside.

Meeting: The President, Haldeman, and Ehrlichman. Oval Office. April 14, 1973.

Many questions were left hanging regarding the relationship between ITT and the Justice Department.

"But, first, a word from our sponsor . . . !"

The Senate judiciary hearings get curiouser and curiouser.

P [Unintelligible] You think—you feel that really the man, the trigger man was Colson on this then?

D Well, no, he was one of the s—, He was just in the chain. He was, he helped push the thing.

P Called them up about it and said, "We've got a, we've got a good plan, hang on with it." Christ, he would be the—oh, I'll bet you, I know why. That was at the time of I.T.T. He was trying to get something going there because I.T.T., they were bugging us. I mean they were—

D Uh.

P Giving us hell.

D Well, I know, I know he used, uh—

P Hunt to go out there?

D Hunt.

P I knew about that.

D Yeah.

P I did know about it. Uh, I knew that there, there was something going on there—

D Right.

P But I didn't know, it was a hunch.

Meeting: The President, Haldeman, and Dean.
Oval Office. March 21, 1973.

"Mrs. Beard is obviously much improved . . . She now categorically denies the ITT memorandum!"

P My guess is the Star pointed out (inaudible) that they—(inaudible). Actually they got the money after the 10th, but I don't think they pointed out that Sears got it before.

D For all purposes, the donor—Vesco—

P Stans would never do a thing like that! Never. Never. Never.

D I think we have a good strong case that the donor had relinquished control of the money, and constructive possession of the money was in the hands of the finance committee, Sears and the like. So that there is not—ah—

P How did they get my brother in it? Eddie?

D That was sheer sandbagging of your brother. Here is what they did. They called him down here in Washington . . .

Meeting: The President and Dean.
Oval Office. February 27, 1973.

D It is just a lot of minutia we've got to go through but he is coming in next week and I told him we would sit down and he is preparing everything—all that is available, and we are going to sit down with Frank DeMarco and see if we can't get this whole thing—

P They can't get his records with regard to his private transactions?

D No, none of the private transactions. Absolutely, that is privileged material. Anything to do with San Clemente and the like—that is just so far out of bounds that—

P Did they ask for them?

D No. No indication.

P Kalmbach is a decent fellow. He will make a good witness.

Meeting: The President and Dean.
Oval Office. February 28, 1973.

GIVE THE GIFT THAT KEEPS ON GIVING...

GIVE YOUR HOME (IMPROVED
WITH MILLIONS OF TAXPAYERS'
DOLLARS) TO THE AMERICAN
PEOPLE. TAX DEDUCTIONS
CAN BE ARRANGED TO BEGIN
WHEN PRESENT WRITE-OFFS
RUN OUT. IMMEDIATE TAX
BENEFITS POSSIBLE.

P You better damned well remember being—The main thing is this, John, and when you meet with the lawyers — and you Bob, and I hope Strachan has been told — believe me — don't try to hedge anything before the damned Grand Jury. I'm not talking about morality, but I'm talking about the vulnerabilities.

E Sure, good advice.

Meeting: The President, Haldeman, Ehrlichman, and Ziegler. Oval Office. April 17, 1973.

Would you trade this used man for a new Ford?

"Have I got a deal for you!"

HP Ah, then you also asked about Colson. Colson and Dean were together with Ehrlichman when Ehrlichman advised about Hunt to get out of town and thereafter—

P Colson was there?

HP Colson was there so he is going to be in the Grand Jury. With respect to Haldeman, another matter. In connection with payments of money after—

P the fact.

HP June 17th, Mitchell requested Dean to activate Kalmbach. Dean said he didn't have that authority and he went to Haldeman.

P Uh, huh.

HP Haldeman gave him the authority.

P Uh, huh.

HP He then got in touch with Kalmbach to arrange for money, the details of which we really don't know as yet.

P Right.

HP So Kalmbach is also a Grand Jury witness to be called. And I think those are the only additional developments.

Telephone Conversation: The President and Petersen. April 16, 1973.

"Alas, poor Agnew, Mitchell, Stans, Ehrlichman, Haldeman, Dean,
Kalmbach, LaRue, Mardian, Strachan, McCord, Liddy, Chapin,
Hunt, Colson, Krogh, Magruder, Young—I knew them . . ."

THE COVER-UP
OF
THE COVER-UP
OF
THE COVER-UP

P John, I'm just trying to see what the options are on Dean—what we turn loose here.

E Absolutely. Well, let's go back to the press plan. Maybe that will give us some guidance.

P Right.

E If you say in the press plan, "The President got concerned about this," the question, "why didn't he get concerned sooner because this has been in the paper for months and months?" Well, "the reason he didn't get concerned sooner is he was resting secure in the belief that he had the whole story."

P Right.

E Well, what made him insecure?

P Do I ever ask Dean in and ask him answers? The answer is no.

E No, but the point is that you were resting secure on his assurances.

P Go ahead.

E Well—

H Didn't you at some point get a report from Dean that nobody in the White House was involved.

E Didn't we put that out way back in August?

P I mean, I just said "Well, that's all I know now." It was never in writing. He never came in orally and told me Dean—John Dean I never saw about this matter. You better check, but I don't think John Dean was ever seen about this matter until I saw him, when John Ehrlichman suggested that I'd better see John Dean.

E You better check Bob, back in that period of time July—when we were in San Clemente—my recollection is that he did come and see you at that time—but we can check that.

P Oh—by himself? No.

E Well, by himself or with one of us. I don't know.

P He may have come in, but it was a pretty—I hope he did, hope he did. But he might have come in sort of the end, and someone said, "Look here's John Dean from Washington," and I may have said, "Thanks for all your hard work."

E Well—let's follow this line and see where it leads us. The President rested secure in the belief that his Counsel had investigated this and assured him that nobody in the White House was involved.

Meeting: The President, Haldeman, Ehrlichman, and Ziegler. Oval Office. April 17, 1973.

HP She said, "Doesn't all this upset you?" And I said, "Of course it does."

P "Why the hell doesn't the President do something?"

HP She said, "Do you think the President knows?" And I looked at her and said, "If I thought the President knew, I would have to resign." But, you know, now there is my own family, Mr. President—

P Sure. Sure.

HP Now whatever confidence she has in you, her confidence in me ought to be unquestioned. Well, when that type of question comes through in my home—

P We've got to get it out.

HP We've got a problem.

P Well you know I have wrestled with it. I've been trying to—

HP Mr. President, I pray for you, sir.

P I have been trying to get the thing. Like even poor Gray—there was nothing we could do. Ah—wrestling with Dean's covers. But ah—

HP I wouldn't try to distinguish between the three of them.

P I understand. I understand. Well, I won't try to distinguish, but maybe they will be handled differently due to the fact that I am not communicating with Dean.

HP Mr. President, it is always easier to advise than it is to assume the responsibility.

P I will do it my way. And it will be done. I am working on it. I won't even tell you how—how—

HP I understand.

Meeting: The President and Petersen.
Oval Office. April 27, 1973.

"I'm not a crook! I've earned everything I've got!"

E   There were 8 or 10 people around here who knew about this, knew it was going on. Bob knew, I knew, all kinds of people knew.

P   Well, I knew it. I knew it.

E   And it was not a question of whether—

P   I must say though, I didn't know it but I must have assumed it though but you know, fortunately—I thank you both for arranging it that way and it does show the isolation of the President, and here it's not so bad—

Meeting: The President, Haldeman, and Ehrlichman. E.O.B. Office. April 14, 1973.

"I KNOW WHAT IS BEST FOR VIETNAM...
I HAVE MORE FACTS."

"I KNOW WHAT IS BEST FOR THE ECONOMY...
I HAVE MORE FACTS."

"I KNOW WHAT IS BEST TO STOP INFLATION...
I HAVE MORE FACTS."

"I KNOW WHAT IS BEST FOR CAMBODIA...
I HAVE MORE FACTS."

"I KNOW WHAT IS BEST FOR AMERICA...
I HAVE MORE FACTS."

"HOW COULD I HAVE KNOWN ABOUT WATERGATE?..
I'M JUST THE PRESIDENT!"

P You didn't know that they were doing this? I didn't know.

K No sir—I didn't know.

P I didn't—you know—as I was—one of the problems here—I have always run my campaigns. I didn't run this one I must say. I was pretty busy.

Meeting: The President and Kleindienst.
E.O.B. Office. April 15, 1973.

"That's about the way it looks from here, Walter . . ."

E I think—no. I think it should be a very tight statement—very conservative—well at least you should think it through so that you can stay away from the soft places. But I think broadly— across the country—people are waiting to see your face on the evening news talking about the Watergate case. And making more assurances.

P Bill Rogers says this (unintelligible) first thought Ziegler—then as we left the boat last night (unintelligible) he totally rules out the 9:00. He says, "Don't make it the only story (unintelligible) 3 or 4 months (unintelligible)."

H You know where the Watergate story is in the Washington Post today? Page 19.

E (unintelligible)

P I know. I know. And it'll be page 19 five months from now if we handle it right.

Meeting: The President, Haldeman, Ehrlichman, and Ziegler. Oval Office. April 17, 1973.

"You are getting weary . . . very weary . . . of Watergate!"

D If he takes it to Kleindienst, Kleindienst is going to say, "Bill just don't do it because you are going to take DeLoach's name down with it, and DeLoach is a friend of ours."

P (Expletive deleted)

D Something I have always thought.

P Nobody is a friend of ours. Let's face it! Don't worry about that sort of thing.

Meeting: The President, Haldeman, and Dean.
Oval Office. March 13, 1973.

"... Rose Mary did it ...!"

P I think he made a very powerful point to me that of course, you can be pragmatic and say, (unintelligible) cut your losses and get rid of 'em. Give 'em an hors d'oeuvre and maybe they won't come back for the main course. Well, out, John Dean.

Meeting: The President, Haldeman, and Ehrlichman. E.O.B. Office. April 14, 1973.

"... Bad dog ... !"

P Another thing. I would like the libel suits. I think both of you, and Bob particularly, you ought to get yourself a libel lawyer, Bob, and check the or have Wilson check and use the most vicious libel lawyer there is. I'd sue every (expletive deleted) (unintelligible). There have been stories over this period of time. That will make—that also helps with public opinion. Sue right down the line. It doesn't make any difference now about the taking depositions and the rest, does it? The important thing is the story's big and I think you ought to go out and sue people for libel.

H Do you mean Senator Weicker?

P He's covered.

E Oh, he's not, not when he was on Issues and Answers.

H (unintelligible) or using newspaper interviews.

E That's right.

H It was not on the Floor, he's too buzzy, stupid.

P The point is the thing with Weicker (unintelligible) is whether he said—how did he say that? Was it libelous?

H I think so. I better ask a lawyer.

P Was he that specific?

H He was damned specific.

P That Haldeman knew?

H Yes. "That Haldeman directed and Haldeman was in personal command of all personnel." I repeat, "all personnel at the Re-election Committee."

P Good, sue him.

E I think you should.

H He said that I was in personal command of Liddy and Hunt.

P I would sue.

H And McCord (unintelligible) I have never met or heard of him.

P John, this libel thing. You may as well get at the libel thing and have yourself a little fun.

Meeting: The President, Rogers, Haldeman, Ehrlichman. E.O.B. Office. April 17, 1973.

"Let others wallow in Watergate . . ."
—President Nixon, July, 1973

P Here's what John is to. You really think you've got to clean the cancer out now, right?

D Yes sir.

P How would you do that? Do you see another way? Without breaking down our executive privilege?

D I see a couple of ways to do it.

P You certainly don't want to do it at the Senate, do you?

D No sir. I think that would be an added trap.

P That's the worst thing. Right. We've got to do it. We aren't asked to do it.

D You've got to do it, to get the credit for it. That gets you above it. As I see it, naturally you'll get hurt and I hope we can find the answer to that problem.

Meeting: The President, Haldeman, and and Dean. E.O.B. Office. March 21, 1973.

"If he gets hurt, it's your fault!"

RZ Woodward said they had two stories; one was the fact that it was reaching a new plateau, and he was not ready to read the story because he was still working on it, and Woodward was taking the position that he was confused and needed to talk to someone to get a perception.

HP They are trying people.

RZ What they are trying to do is to get a fix on what's happened over here.

P OK. Take a hard line. Gergen to Woodward. Anything on that they better watch their damned cotton picking faces. Because boy, if there's one thing in this case as Henry will tell you, since March 21st when I had that conversation with Dean, I have broken my ass to try to get the facts of this case. Right? Tried to get that damn Liddy to talk. We tried to get—finally got Gray to refresh his memory. (unintelligible)

Meeting: The President, Ziegler, and Petersen.
Oval Office. April 27, 1973.

"I'm OK, you're OK!"

P The next part is what I'm concerned about. "I began new inquiries," shall we say?

E Well, I don't know.

P "I began new inquiries into this matter as a result of serious charges which were reported publicly and privately." Should we say that?

E Publicly, comma "which in some cases were reported publicly."

P "Four weeks ago we," Why don't we say, shall we set a date? That sounds a hell of a lot stronger if we set a date.

E All right.

P "On March 21, I began new inquiries," Strike that. "I ordered an investigation, new inquiries throughout the government—"

Meeting: The President, Haldeman, Ehrlichman, and Ziegler. Oval Office. April 17, 1973.

"I'm sorry—I don't recognize any of them . . . !"

"Who wouldn't believe those lips, who wouldn't believe those eyes, the night you told me, those little White House lies."

P It will be somewhat serious but the main thing, of course, if also the isolation of the President.

D Absolutely! Totally true!

P Because that, fortunately, is totally true.

D I know that sir!

Meeting: The President and Dean.
Oval Office. February 27, 1973.

On the beach

P John Dean, please.

OPR Yes, Mr. President.

P Hello.

D Yes, Sir.

P You are having rather long days these days, aren't you? I guess we all have.

D I think they will continue to be longer.

Telephone Conversation: The President and Dean.
March 20, 1973.

Sunset off San Clemente

P Have you thought when you say before it gets to (unintelligible) thing out of the way. Have you given any thought to what the line ought to be—I don't mean a lie—but a line, on raising the money for these defendants? Because both of you were aware of what was going on you see—the raising of the money—you were aware of it, right?

E Yes, sir.

P And you were aware—You see, you can't go in and say I didn't know what in hell he wanted the $250 for.

H No—I've given a great deal of thought (unintelligible)

P Well I wonder. I'm not—look—I'm concerned about the legal thing Bob, and so forth. You say that our purpose was to keep them from talking to the press.

E Well, that was my purpose—and before I get too far out on that, ah, I want to talk to an attorney and find out what the law is—which I have not yet done.

P Right!

H That's just what I want to do too.

Meeting: The President, Haldeman, Ehrlichman, and Ziegler. Oval Office. April 17, 1973.

"I'd like to see my lawyer . . ."

H And the panel is empowered to act to remove anybody that it sees fit because of involvement, to level fines and to impose criminal sanctions. The defendants in the Watergate trial, the men who have already been—can also submit any information that they want.

P Right.

H Anyone who does not submit to the proceedings of this committee under these conditions—

P Resign.

Meeting: The President, Haldeman, Ehrlichman, and Ziegler. E.O.B. Office. March 27, 1973.

"I accept the responsibility
and I resign."
—Willy Brandt

"I accept the responsibility
but I will not resign."
—Richard Nixon

THE WHITE HOUSE

WASHINGTON

April 1, 1974

Members of the Congress
The Capitol
Washington, D.C.

Sirs:

Although innocent of all charges and confident
of acquittal in whatever impeachment proceedings
you might bring against me, I believe it is time
to put Watergate behind us. I herewith submit
my resignation as President of the United States.

Respectfully yours,

Richard Nixon

Richard M. Nixon
President of the United States

APRIL FOOL!

"Impeachable source"

P I told Ruck, incidentally, that he was to coop-erate with the investigation and I said, "Ruck you are to do anything that the prosecutor says to do, Henry Petersen, or the prosecutors, leave no stone unturned and I don't give a damn who it hurts. Now believe me, that's what he's been told. So you got a man there who will—

HP I know him and I think well of him, Mr. President.

P Well, he's Mr. Clean, you know so you understand —

HP Yes, indeed. He's quite able, he is indeed.

P So there you are. You've got to knock that—Crack down. If there's one thing you have got to do, you have got to maintain the Presidency out of this. I have got things to do for this country and I'm not going to have—now this is per-sonal. I sometimes feel like I'd like to resign. Let Agnew be President for a while. He'd love it.

Meeting: The President and Petersen.
Oval Office. April 27, 1973.

CAPTAIN RICHARD M. QUEEG

"You don't have to worry about me getting seasick or jumping ship! I'm staying at the helm until we bring it into port!"

D There are two routes. One is to figure out how to cut the losses and minimize the human impact and get you up and out and away from it in any way. In a way it would never come back to haunt you. That is one general alternative. The other is to go down the road, just hunker down, fight it at every corner, every turn, don't let people testify—cover it up is what we really are talking about. Just keep it buried, and just hope that we can do it, hope that we make good decisions at the right time, keep our heads cool, we make the right moves.

P And just take the heat?

D And just take the heat.

Meeting: The President, Dean, and Haldeman.
Oval Office. March 21, 1973.

"If you want me, you're gonna have to come and get me!"

P Dean. You will get Dean in there. Suppose he starts trying to impeach the President, the word of the President of the United States and says, "Well, I have information to the effect that I once discussed with the President the question of how the possibility, of the problem," of this damn Bittman stuff I spoke to you about last time. Henry, it won't stand up for five minutes because nothing was done, and fortunately I had Haldeman at that conversation and he was there and I said, "Look, I tried to give you this, this, this, this, this and this." And I said, "When you finally get it out, it won't work. Because," I said, "First, you can't get clemency to Hunt."

HP I agree.

P I mean, I was trying to get it out. To try to see what that—Dean had been doing! I said, "First you can't give him clemency." Somebody has thrown out something to the effect that Dean reported that Hunt had an idea that he was going to get clemency around Christmas. I said, "Are you kidding? You can't get clemency for Hunt. You couldn't even think about it until, you know, '75 or something like that." Which you could, then because of the fact, that you could get to the—ah—But nevertheless, I said you couldn't give clemency. I said, "The second point to remember is 'How are you going to get the money for them?' If you could do it, I mean you are talking about a million dollars." I asked him—well, I gave him several ways. I said, "You couldn't put it through a Cuban Committee could you?" I asked him, because to me he was sounding so damned ridiculous. I said, "Well under the circumstances," I said, "There isn't a damn thing we can do." I said, "It looks to me like the problem is sue John Mitchell." Mitchell came down the next day and we talked about executive privilege. Nothing else. Now, that's the total story. And—so Dean—I just want you to be sure that if Dean ever raises the thing, you've got the whole thing. You've got that whole thing. Now kick him straight—.

Meeting: The President, Petersen, and Ziegler.
Oval Office. April 27, 1973.

P Good, good. How has the scenario worked out? May I ask you?

H Well, it works out very good. You became aware sometime ago that this thing did not parse out the way it was supposed to and that there were some discrepancies between what you had been told by Dean in the report that there was nobody in the White House involved, which may still be true.

P Incidentally, I don't think it will gain us anything by dumping on the Dean Report as such.

E No.

P What I mean is I would say I was not satisfied that the Dean Report was complete and also I thought it was my obligation to go beyond that to people other than the White House.

E Ron has an interesting point. Remember you had John Dean go to Camp David to write it up. He came down and said, "I can't."

P Right.

E That is the tip off and right then you started to move.

P That's right. He said he could not write it.

H Then you realized that there was more to this than you had been led to believe. (unintelligible)

P How do I get credit for getting Magruder to the stand?

Meeting: The President, Haldeman, and Ehrlichman. Oval Office. April 16, 1973.

Would you buy a used transcript from this man?

D I am not talking about documents you see. I am talking about something we can spread as facts. You see you could even write a novel with the facts.

P (Inaudible)

D (Inaudible)

P (Inaudible)

Meeting: The President, Haldeman, Ehrlichman, Dean, and Mitchell. E.O.B. Office. March 21, 1973.

("Some sinister force"
erased this cartoon.)

"...Hummmmmmmmmm...!"

White House transcript

D Everyone is getting their own counsel. More counsel are getting involved. How do I protect my ass?

P They are scared.

D That is bad. We were able to hold it for a long time. Another thing is that my facility to deal with the multitude of people I have been dealing with has been hampered . . .

Judiciary Committee transcript

D Everyone is getting their own counsel. More counsel are getting involved. How do I protect my ass?

P They're scared.

D They're scared and that's just, you know, that's bad. We were able to hold it for a long time.

P Yeah, I know.

D Uh, another thing . . .

Meeting: The President, Haldeman, and Dean. Oval Office. March 21, 1973.

"Blessed are those who have not heard, but still believe me!"

E Wednesday. You should put my statement out on Wednesday also, or wait until Thursday for my statement. I think we better be right out in the open—

P That's right. I'd put yours out right with it. You're going to have the next day to build it up a little.

H No—you don't want to build it up.

P Put it right out. The problem here, let me say, in your case, is not Segretti. I think we should go with the Segretti stuff and then—the problem in your case is Strachan. I mean the—keeping the (unintelligible).

H (Unintelligible)

Meeting: The President, Haldeman, and Ehrlichman. E.O.B. Office. April 14, 1973.

P All right. We have got the immunity problem resolved. Do it. Dean if you need to, but boy I am telling you—there ain't going to be any blackmail.

HP Mr. President, I—

P Don't let Dick Kleidienst say it. Dean ain't— "Hunt is going to blackmail you." Hunt's not going to blackmail any of us. "It is his word, basically, against yours." It's his word against mine. Now for—who is going to believe John Dean? We relied on the damned so—Dean, Dean was the one who told us throughout the summer that nobody in the White House was involved when he, himself apparently, was involved, particularly on the critical angle of subornation of perjury. That's the one that—I will never, never understand John.

Meeting: The President and Petersen.
Oval Office. April 27, 1973.

"Now, confidentially speaking . . ."

H If we have to get out of here, I think the Foun-
tion funding—is one thing—but there is a lot of
intrigue too — I hope to get funding for the
ability to clear my name and spend the rest of
my life destroying what some people like Dean
and Magruder have done to the President.

*Meeting: The President, Haldeman, Ehrlichman
and Rogers. E.O.B. Office. April 17, 1973.*

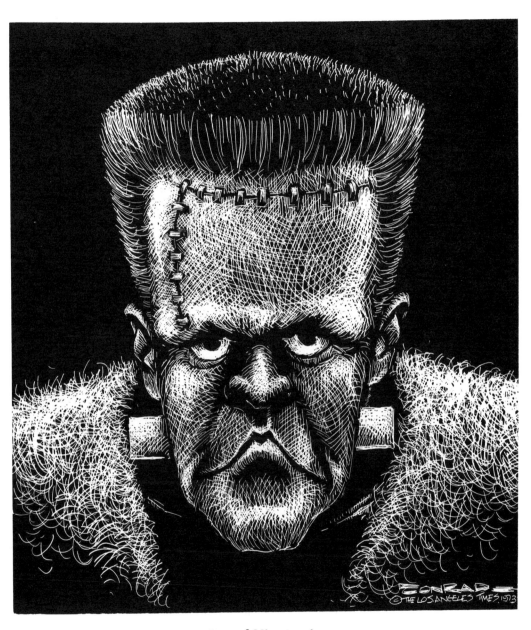

Son of Nixonstein

E Well, as I said before. We beat the rap but we're damaged goods.

P Right, you can't go back in the government, but I will tell you one thing, you are not damaged goods as far as I am concerned. It's one hell of a thing. The point is that let's wait and see what happens before we see where we are.

H Sure.

P We ought to expect the worst but I think that what I would like both of you to consider 50% of your time also for editing etc., and so on, with the Foundation. The Foundation is going to be a hell of a big thing, it's bound to be. These first four years are terribly important and so forth.

Meeting: The President, Haldeman, Ehrlichman, and Rogers. E.O.B. Office. April 17, 1973.

"...FOUR MORE YEARS!...FOUR MORE YEARS!..."

W It's nice to talk to you even under these circumstances.

P Well, we hope that by Golly—that we'll talk under better—

S Last time I saw you it was crowded—out at the Wardman Park—the Shoreham—I could have lifted my feet off the floor and watched you—you and your family on the podium.

P What was that?

S That was election night.

P Election night—you were there? Oh boy. That was a great night? Well, that was what it was all about.

S Yes, it sure was.

P Well, we'll survive this. You know—people say this destroys the Administration and the rest—but what was this? What was Watergate? A little bugging! I mean a terrible thing — it shouldn't have been done— shouldn't have been covered up. And people shouldn't have and the rest, but we've got to beat it. Right.

Meeting: The President, Wilson, and Strickler.
E.O.B. Office. April 19, 1973.

Would you buy a used mandate from this man?

P OK Now—this brings us to a basic command decision with regard—with regard to what you do about White House people. The main thing is (inaudible) and you can look at it in terms of the fact that anybody who this touches should go out—without—(inaudible). You can look at it in terms of the fact that if it touches them (inaudible) that clearly apart from whether or not anything legal stands up. Let's suppose—just take Ehrlichman is a case in point—that this thing brought in by (inaudible) that proves to be (inaudible) don't get anything else on Ehrlichman then the question is that nevertheless that in itself would raise a cloud over Ehrlichman. That would mean that he would be no longer be useful. Therefore, your advice—on Sunday or least it was now—sack Haldeman, Ehrlichman and Dean now—all three—because in the one case Dean should know he has admitted complicity—in the other case there is a possibility of charges which may not be true and which may not be indictable but which from the standpoint of the public will so involve them that it will cut off their legs. And let me say—I understand the point as well—the only thing is the question of how and when you do it—and as that I (inaudible). And so I have decided to handle each on an individual basis—and by that I mean that our policy generally will be that anyone who refused to cooperate will, of course, be sacked immediately.

Meeting: The President and Petersen.
Oval Office. April 17, 1973.

"Hand over those tapes or you're fired!"

D Because it will put them in context of where government institutes were used in the past for the most flagrant political purposes.

P How can that help us?

D How does it help us?

P I am being the devil's advocate . . .

D I appreciate what you are doing.

Meeting: The President, Haldeman, and Dean.
Oval Office. March 13, 1973.

The Exorcist

Well, back to the "sinister force" theory . . .

P Who all have you seen this morning?

E Well, I have Strachan up there right now.

P Yeah. I had a call from Kleindienst.

E Yeah. I heard you did and I thought you ought to take it. He—

P O sure, sure, I did. I didn't refuse. He said "I should see you, and I'd like to see you alone this afternoon. Today." I said fine. He's coming to the church service.

Meeting: The President and Ehrlichman.
Oval Office. April 15, 1973.

"All those wishing to make a 'decision for Nixon'
will please come forward . . ."

D You know, with me there was no way, but the burden of this second Administration is something that is not going to go away.

P No, it isn't.

D It is not going to go away, Sir!

P It is not going to go away.

D Exactly.

Meeting: The President, Haldeman, and Dean.
Oval Office. March 21, 1973.

(Like Sisyphus, doomed forever to push a rock up a steep hill. Just
before it reaches the top, it plunges back to the bottom, so
that his wearying task never ends.)

E The thing that I get over and over and over again from just ordinary folks—

P Right.

E "Why doesn't the President," so and so and so and so.

P "Say something what's he done on it?"

E Yeah. So symbolically you've got to do something.

P That's right. Do something so that I am out front on this every—they don't think the President is involved but they don't think he is doing enough.

E That's it. That's it.

P No matter how often we say we will cooperate —as you know we have done—and on and on and on —

Meeting: The President, Haldeman, Ehrlichman, and Ziegler. E.O.B. Office. March 27, 1973.

Another new Nixon

P I was talking to Bob—and Bob made the point—he said, well just look at what will happen here. In a sense it will be the evening news basically—you know what I mean—they are not going to run it live—not now on the nets. And also there are chances of how much the committee can do, particularly with Mitchell, if he hires somebody—an attorney enjoining—, it could go on for a while. But the point is—Bob says you will have either seven minutes of John Chancellor and Weicker interpreting what was said in a secret session or do you want four minutes of that and maybe three minutes of Haldeman?

E Well, that is a good point.

P Is that something to be considered?

E It sure is. At least we get a little piece of it that way.

P You know—you see a man looking honest and earnest etc., denying it in a public forum—

E Yeah, yeah.

P Where he just—you know I just have a feeling—

E There is something to be said for splitting the time with them.

P Yes and—

E Are you planning to work tomorrow?

P Well I tell you — sure — what I plan to do — I have to do church.

E Sure.

Telephone Conversation: The President and Ehrlichman. April 14, 1973.

Father John McLaughlin, exorcist

P Your major guy to keep under control is Hunt?

D That is right.

P I think. Does he know a lot?

D He knows so much. He could sink Chuck Colson. Apparently he is quite distressed with Colson. He thinks Colson has abandoned him. Colson was to meet with him when he was out there after, you know, he had left the White House. He met with him through his lawyer. Hunt raised the question he wanted money. Colson's lawyer told him Colson wasn't doing anything with money. Hunt took offense with that immediately, and felt Colson had abandoned him.

P Just looking at the immediate problem, don't you think you have to handle Hunt's financial situation damn soon?

D I think that is—I talked with Mitchell about that last night and—

P It seems to me we have to keep the cap on the bottle that much, or we don't have any options.

D That's right.

P Either that or it blows right now?

Meeting: The President, Haldeman and Dean.
Oval Office. March 21, 1973.

"Blessed is the President: for he shall be found innocent.
    Blessed is the Judiciary Committee: for it shall obey our commandments.
    Blessed are the tapes: for they shall not see the light of day . . ."

H That is where your dangers lie, in all these stupid human errors developing.

P Sure. The point is Bob, let's face it, the secretaries, the assistants know all of this. The principals may be as hard as a rock, but you never know when they, or some of their people may crack. But, we'll see, we'll see. Here we have the Hunt problem that ought to be handled now.

Meeting: The President, Dean, and Haldeman.
Oval Office. March 21, 1973.

"Who's responsible for all these leaks?"

Z (Inaudible) you said that? We face a situation where—

P They'll run to—

Z They will—have you said this?—we will face the situation number one (inaudible) conclusions about the scope of this (inaudible). Those people who are holding information will be under great pressure to move quickly with whatever they have.

Meeting: The President, Petersen, and Ziegler.
E.O.B. Office. April 16, 1973.

(The object of "streaking" is to run nude through
a public place without quite being seen.)

P Does (unintelligible) know Bob. Aren't we really sort of in a position where it would be better to know whose (unintelligible) in that damn Grand Jury. At least, pull the (unintelligible) on something there. I really think you do. And, they're (unintelligible) happy. It seems to me that a hell of a lot of the issue about do something involves our inability to (unintelligible) back that we're willing to cooperate. That we're willing to waive executive privilege and keeping our people silent. Now that's what I'm really trying to (unintelligible).

E We will get—

H I've always heard that that's the right—that's the point—that kind of argument.

P Is that (unintelligible).

H (Unintelligible) one day plus story.

P Yeah.

H The price for which is weeks of—

P Disaster.

H Disaster.

E But the thing that's wrong with that is that while it's a one day plus story, it's also the illumination of ninety days of negative stories.

P Before you ever get there. That's the point.

H And it's setting up ninety days of other negative, more negative stories.

E Well, maybe. Maybe. That's a very good question.

P The question is how much more negative is there.

Meeting: The President, Haldeman, and Ehrlichman. Oval Office. April 14, 1973.

"It'll sure put an end to the leaks!"

P Yeah. (inaudible)—keep in my mind—(inaudible) get the damn thing over with—and I know the trials of Mitchell and all these people will take a long time—(inaudible)—Mitchell will never plead guilty, never. Fight it all the way down the line (inaudible). What would you do if you were Mitchell?

HP I think I would probably go to Saudi Arabia to tell you the truth.

Meeting: The President and Petersen.
Oval Office. April 17, 1973.

"Ron, which countries on my trip don't have
extradition treaties with us?"

The King is dead . . . long live the Presidency!